Adventures in Cartooning
Christmas Special

James Sturm

Andrew Arnold

Alexis Frederick-Frost

SCHOLASTIC INC.

Don't kids still enjoy the printed page?

My elves may have gone to MIT, but 'ol Santa still knows how to tell a story!

I KNOW! A Christmas gift as a COMIC!

That is the perfect holiday tonic!

I require an elf with comic book chops...

But can he be found in my workshop?

Your fantastic exploits—they should do the trick! Now tell me, brave knight, what makes you tick?

Um, no offense Santa, but kids don't like getting books as presents—and rhyming books are even **WORSE!**

HEY. Since when is a book that rhymes such a **CURSE?**

NO MORE RHYMING!! **ENOUGH** is **ENOUGH!**

Well, I like to rhyme, so tough, TOUGH, **TOUGH.**

UGGHH! **STOP IT!!!** I **REALLY** MEAN IT THIS TIME!

No, you cannot get ME to stop speaking in rhyme.

Sigh...

14

Let's start with the boldest of expeditions: climbing Mount Everest in the direst conditions!

As I reached the summit, the blizzard did blast!
The cold numbed my body...

How long can I last?!

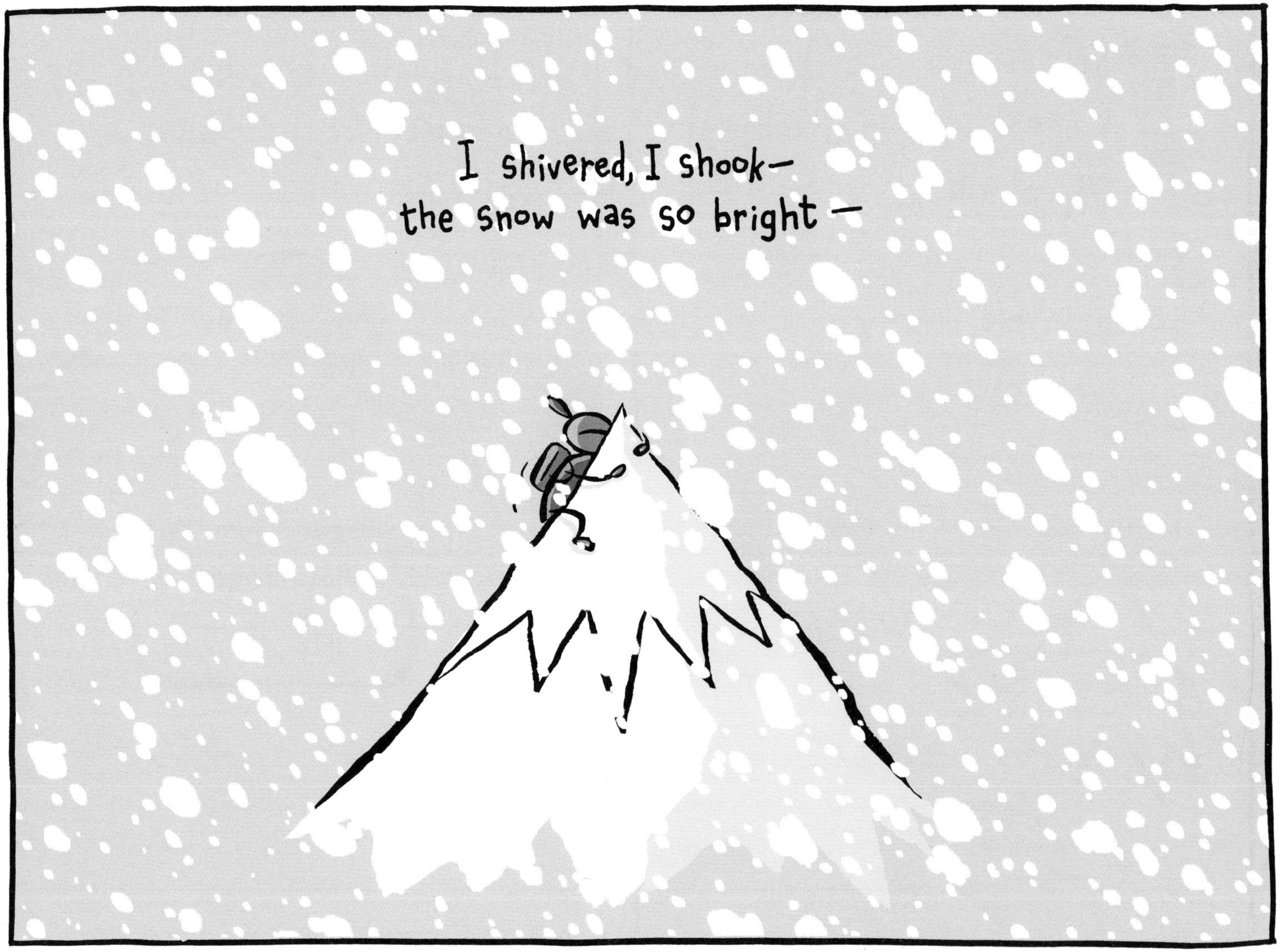
I shivered, I shook—
the snow was so bright—

I thought I'd black out,
but then it all

just

went

white...

When I awoke things were even more dire! Out of the frying pan—into the fire!

I had been captured by the mysterious yeti...

...who tried to eat me like a piece of spaghetti!

I moved lightning fast to thwart his attack: grabbed a bone from the floor and...

WHACK! WHACK! WHACK!

Okay, Mister Yeti, not to be rude, but I **REFUSE** to be your food!

FOOD?! Don't be absurd!!! I wouldn't eat you!

Sucking an arm is how yetis greet you!

Once we cleared things up, we sat down and fed— a slow-roasted goat on a loaf of fresh bread.

YUM!

20

Your harrowing tale has no holiday theme...

Hmm, yeah, you're right. I see what you mean.

A Christmas story must have a **DEEP MEANING.**

Something inspiring!

Something redeeming!

Like...a man who has always been cruel and greedy learns to be kind, and gives to the needy!

I find that kind of story quite sappy. I'll tell you one that's a little more snappy!

In the land of the giants,
the kids like to play.
They build giant snow-
men and ride giant sleighs.

But the most impressive thing of all is a Christmas tree TEN MILES TALL!

There were SO MANY stars, each one of great worth,

but I picked out the brightest to take down to earth!

On Christmas morning a great miracle was seen—
all of the children turned off their screens.
They took out some paper and started to draw...

...the things they imagined...

...and things that they saw.

cat

Monsters and heroes were sketched into boxes...

...and robots and rockets...

...and even some foxes!

The only thing needed to make comics glow is imagination and... and...

a...

Hmm... What rhymes with glow?

A **BIG** TOE!

And with that, dear reader, we finish our tale!

LOOK AT MY BIG TOENAIL!

END

Children used to write me all year long...

Now, I barely get any mail at all!!!

Sniff.

Did...did I do something wrong?

Nothing left to be said. Guess I'll just wash up and go back to bed.

Oh, my!

I can't stand to see Santa cry!!!

<u>Every</u> kid needs to send him a letter!

WAIT! A COMIC STRIP TO SANTA WOULD BE EVEN BETTER!

CALLING ALL KIDS! IT'S NOW UP TO YOU!

Grab some pencils and pens and crayons, too!

Find some paper! (Recycled will do!!!)

Or draw a special vacation OR a favorite food!

This will put Santa in a better mood!

Put your comic in an envelope with a stamp for the toll.

Send to this address—it's half way to the North Pole!

RETURN ADDRESS

COMIC FOR SANTA
THE CENTER FOR CARTOON STUDIES
P.O. BOX 125
WHITE RIVER JUNCTION, VT
05001

—Special thanks to Charlotte, Eva, Isabel, and Sage
for contributing some great drawings!

—And thanks to Calista for her rhyme massages,
it was like sending the book to an awesome spa!!!

ISBN 978-0-545-52207-6

12 11 10 9 8 7 6 5 4 3 2 1   12 13 14 15 16 17/0

Printed in the U.S.A.   08

First Scholastic printing, November 2012